To: _____

From: _____

# The Friends' Night Before Christmas

BY ELLEN WEISS

ILLUSTRATED BY NINA EDWARDS

Peter Pauper Press, Inc.
WHITE PLAINS, NEW YORK

Illustrations copyright © 2003 Nina Edwards

Designed by Heather Zschock

Copyright © 2003
Peter Pauper Press, Inc.
202 Mamaroneck Avenue
White Plains, NY 10601
ISBN 0-88088-337-5
Printed in China
7 6 5 4 3 2 1
Visit us at www.peterpauper.com

# The Friends' Night Before Christmas

'Twas the night before Christmas, and up at the Pole, The Workshop was just about out of control.

The elves were
on overtime,
working away,

Finishing gifts
to be packed
on the sleigh.

There were
dolls to be painted
and shirts to
be sewn;

The kites
needed tails or
they couldn't
be flown.

The trucks needed
fenders, the cars
needed wheels,

The bats needed
sanding, the boats
needed keels.

The boss elf made
sure every item
was packed.
There wasn't a
present that Santa's
sleigh lacked.

He stood with
his clipboard
and checked
off each one;

At last,
after midnight,
the whole job
was done.

When the
Big Guy had
dashed away
into the West,

The elves would go home for a well-deserved rest.

They'd be with
their families,
they'd sleep and
they'd eat,

They'd yawn and they'd put up their little elf feet.

But one little elf
by the name
of Doreen
Went home
to a totally
different scene.

Her kitchen
was quiet, her
table was clear.

Her house was so
still there was
nothing to hear.

No fabulous
smells wafted
out of her stove,

And under her tree there was no treasure trove.

The reason,
of course,
was that this
little elf

Lived simply
and peacefully,
all by herself.

For most
of the year,
she was very
content

To have no
one else who
was splitting
her rent.

Doreen had
her work and
her friends
and her cat,
And the big
reading chair
where she
happily sat.

But she
had to admit,
when the
holidays
came,

That her
life was
the tiniest,
smallest
bit tame.

She wished for
some action,
She wished for
some spice—

A small touch
of chaos would
surely be nice.

The steady
and stable life
did have its
place, But she
yearned now for
something to
make her
heart race.

She looked at
her friends'
houses, glowing
and bright,

And felt a bit
lonesome and
sad at the
sight.

As she stared
out her window,
while having
a think,

She saw something—something that caused her to blink.

Out on
the lawn,
there
appeared
a great
crowd.

It was all
of her buddies,

and boy were
they loud!

There was
Rudy and
Freddie and
Edna and Tess,

Augie and
Reggie and
Stella and Bess.

carrying
presents, by
ones and
by twos,

They marched
through the
snow in their
curly-toed
shoes.

"Wake up!"
they all yelled,
" 'cause the party
is here!

your life has
been too bleepin'
quiet all year!

Time for
some silliness!
Time for some
mess! Forget
saying no,
'cause you have
to say yes!"

In came
the turkey,
and in came
the hams,

In came the
green beans
and squashes
and yams.

They stoked
up the fire till
the kitchen
was warm.

They sang
and they danced
as they cooked
up a storm.

While dinner
was roasting
they brought
out the games.

There was
Whist and Charades
and You-Can't-
Guess-My-Name.

There were card
games and board
games and ball
games and jacks,
and crackers and
cheeses on platters
for snacks.

When dinner was ready they sat at the table

And ate even
more than they
thought they
were able.

While laughing and singing and clinking their glasses

And munching
on gingersnaps
made with
molasses.

They sat and
they talked as
the candles
burned down.
They spoke of
their love for
their little
elf town.

And talked
of their craft,

# of the making
# of toys

For Santa
to bring to the

earth's girls
and boys.

At last it was
time for the
party to end.

Doreen hardly
knew how to
thank her good
friends.

"you'd do it
for us, so we
did it for you.

No need to
say thanks,"
they said,
"that's what
friends do!"

When the
kitchen
was tidied,
the friends
had to go.

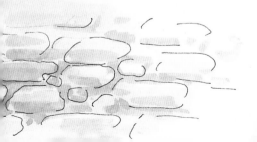

It was time for the elves to walk home through the snow.

And she called
as she waved and
she turned out
the light,

"Merry
christmas to
all, and to all a
good night!"